# THE MAHABHARATA
CHILDREN'S ILLUSTRATED CLASSICS

# THE WAR of KURUKSHETRA

*Retold by* **CHARU AGARWAL DHANDIA**
*Art* **KAVITA SINGH KALE** *Design* **RACHITA RAKYAN**

Published by
Rupa Publications India Pvt. Ltd 2020
7/16, Ansari Road, Daryaganj
New Delhi 110002

*Sales centres:*
Allahabad Bengaluru Chennai
Hyderabad Jaipur Kathmandu
Kolkata Mumbai

Edition copyright © Rupa Publications Pvt. Ltd 2020

All rights reserved.
No part of this publication may be reproduced, transmitted,
or stored in a retrieval system, in any form or by any means, electronic, mechanical, photocopying, recording or otherwise,
without the prior permission of the publisher.

ISBN: 978-81-291-4978-7

First impression 2020

10 9 8 7 6 5 4 3 2 1

The moral right of the author has been asserted.

Printed at Nutech Print Services - India

This book is sold subject to the condition that it shall not, by way of trade or otherwise, be lent, resold, hired out, or otherwise circulated, without the publisher's prior consent, in any form of binding or cover other than that in which it is published.

**Charu Agarwal Dhandia** weaves together her two biggest passions—studying Indian classical literature and creative storytelling. She is an economist by training and works in the social development space.

**Kavita Singh Kale's** background as an artist and a designer enables her to draw a thin line between design following functionality and pure self-expression. This has helped her evolve as a transmedia artist. Her work includes art installations, children's books, comics, paintings and videos.

**Rachita Rakyan** combines over 15 years of expertise in graphic design and art direction with deep understanding of functionality and aesthetics across print, publishing, branding and digital media.

# CONTENTS

| | |
|---|---|
| *KURU DYNASTY* | *IV-V* |
| *KEY CHARACTERS* | *VI-VII* |
| THE WAR BEGINS | 1 |
| ARJUNA ATTACKS BHISHMA | 7 |
| DRONACHARYA ATTACKS YUDHISHTHIRA | 17 |
| CHAKRAVYUH | 23 |
| SUDARSHAN CHAKRA | 31 |
| KARNA, THE NEW CHIEF | 43 |

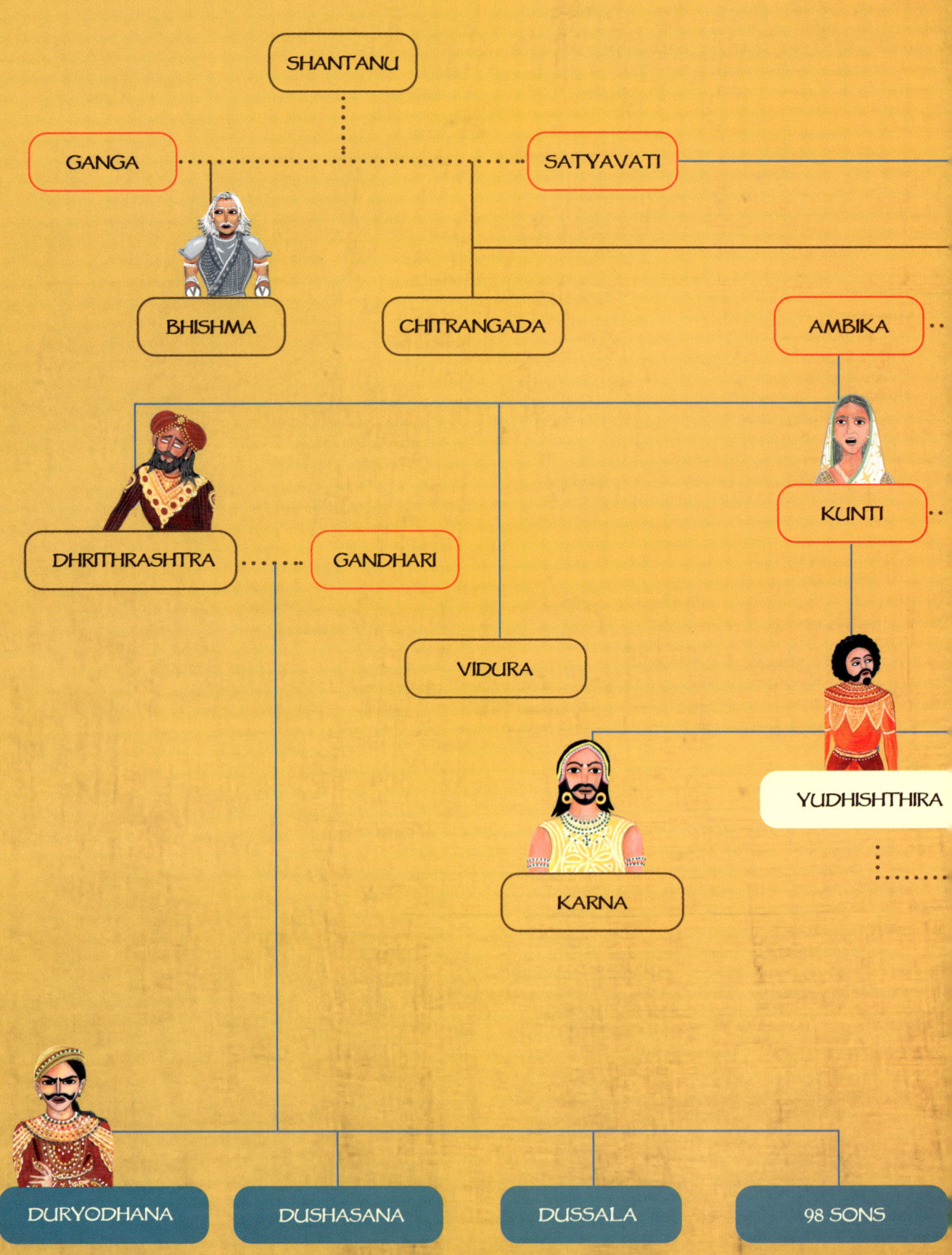

# KURU DYNASTY

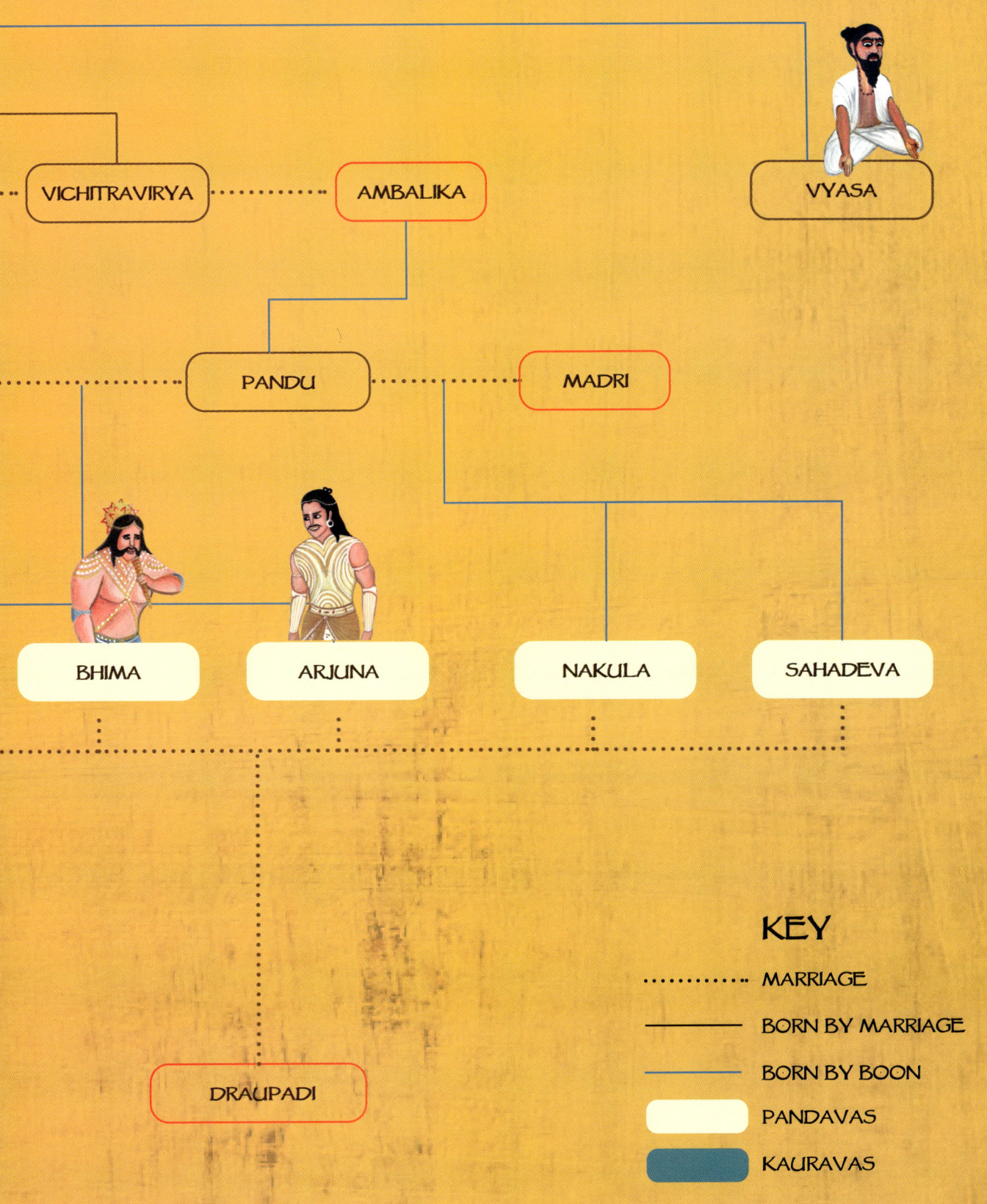

# KEY CHARACTERS

## DURYODHANA

Duryodhana was the eldest brother amongst the Kauravas and born to princess Gandhari as a blessing from sage Vyasa. He was very jealous of the Pandavas.

## YUDHISHTHIRA

Yudhishthira was the eldest Pandava born to Kunti as a blessing from Lord Dharma. He ruled Indraprashtha and later Hastinapur. Yudhishthira proved to be a great ruler and was known for his virtues of honesty, loyalty, justice, tolerance and brotherhood.

## ARJUNA

Arjuna was the third of the Pandava brothers, born to Kunti by the boon of Lord Indra. He was the greatest archer in the country. Arjuna was Dronacharya's favourite pupil.

# KRISHNA

Krishna was the prince of Dwarka and cousin brother of the Pandavas and Kauravas. He was a great friend and advisor to Arjuna and loved the Pandavas dearly. He played a critical role in the creation of Indraprastha and later in the Kurukshetra War.

# KARNA

Karna was born to young Kunti by the boon of Lord Surya. He was raised by a charioteer named Adhiratha and his wife Radha. Later, he became a supremely skilled archer known for his loyalty and his friendship with Duryodhana.

# BHISHMA

Born as Devavrata to King Shantanu and Goddess Ganga, he came to be known as Bhishma, meaning the firm. He was an unparalleled archer and the greatest warrior of that time.

# THE WAR BEGINS

The Pandavas had lost everything to the Kauravas and lived in exile for thirteen years. When the mighty Krishna asked the eldest Kaurava Duryodhana to return Indraprastha to the Pandavas, Duryodhana refused and wanted the Pandavas to win back their kingdom in a battle. So the War of Kurukshetra was declared.

The brave Bhishma became the chief of the Kaurava army. Prince Dhrishtadyumna led the Pandava army. And the war began. The Kaurava army attacked the Pandavas with all their might. The Pandava army fought back mightily.

After a few days of warfare, Duryodhana began to lose patience. He called Bhishma Pitamah and rudely said, 'I made you the chief of the Kaurava army so that we could easily defeat the Pandavas. But we are losing soldiers every day! What are you doing?'

Bhishma calmly replied, 'The Pandavas are very brave. They possess very powerful weapons given to them by various Gods. Even then, I promise you victory very soon!'

# ARJUNA ATTACKS BHISHMA

One day, Arjuna asked Krishna, 'How can we defeat the brave Bhishma?'

'Bhishma is immortal. He has the boon to choose the time of his death. The only person who can defeat Bhishma is Shikandi,' said Krishna. 'Bhishma will never fight Shikandi. Let me tell you a story.'

"In his previous birth, Shikandi was born as Princess Amba. Bhishma had brought her to marry Vichitravirya. When she wanted to marry Bhishma, he refused. Amba believed that Bhishma had ruined her life and she sought revenge. For many years, she prayed to Lord Shiva. Finally, Lord Shiva gave her a boon that she would defeat Bhishma."

It was now the tenth day of the war. Krishna drove Arjuna's chariot right behind Shikandi. He knew that Bhishma would not attack Shikandi. The moment Bhishma tried to attack Arjuna, Shikandi came in his way.

Then, Arjuna aimed at Bhishma and hit a volley of arrows at him. Thousands of arrows pierced Bhishma and formed a bed on which Bhishma collapsed. Men from both the armies stopped and looked at the great warrior Bhishma lying wounded on a bed of arrows.

Then the mighty Bhishma spoke, 'The war is not over and I cannot die. It is my duty to ensure that Hastinapur is safe.' Everybody was silent.

Bhishma turned to Arjuna, 'Son, I am thirsty.' Arjuna shot an arrow into the ground. At once, a stream of water came gushing out and flowed into Bhishma's mouth. He drank some water and closed his eyes.

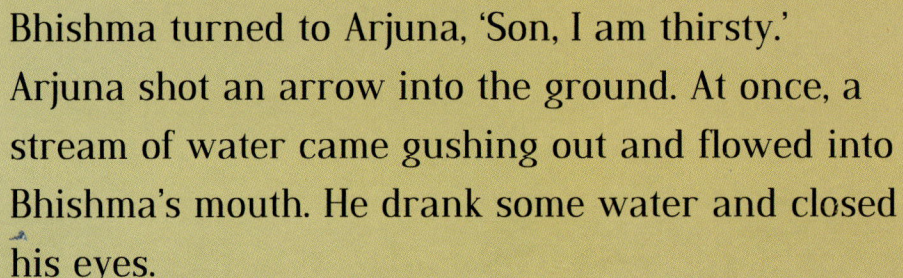

Bhishma was wounded and Duryodhana needed a new chief. Karna joined the Kaurava army. He said to Duryodhana, Dronacharya has taught the Pandavas all their archery and warrior skills.

'No one can attack the Pandavas better than their guru.
Dronacharya should lead the Kaurava army now.'
Duryodhana agreed and Dronacharya became the new chief.

# DRONACHARYA ATTACKS YUDHISHTHIRA

It was the eleventh day of war. Duryodhana called Dronacharya and said, 'Today we need to attack Yudhishthira.'

'The mighty Arjuna has been protecting Yudhishthira,' replied Dronacharya. 'To attack Yudhishthira, we need to keep Arjuna away from him.'

Duryodhana thought of a plan. He would use the band of brave soldiers called Samsaptakas. 'They will attack Arjuna from all sides so that he cannot protect Yudhishthira,' he said.

The next day, hundreds of Samsaptakas attacked Arjuna but he fought back bravely. Dronacharya took this opportunity to come close to Yudhishthira's chariot to attack him. But before he could shoot an arrow, Arjuna reached Yudhishthira. Arjuna had defeated all the Samsaptakas!

Then Arjuna and Yudhishthira fought the Kaurava army with all their might.

Night fell and the day ended.

# CHAKRAVYUH

That evening, Duryodhana was very angry. He called Dronacharya and roared, 'You had promised to hold Yudhishthira captive. But you have failed!'

'Forgive me, Duryodhana, I got close but Arjuna rescued him today. However, I have a plan for tomorrow,' replied Dronacharya.

The next morning, Dronacharya arranged his army in the shape of a lotus. It would be impossible to enter or come out of the *Chakravyuh*. Hundreds of soldiers, horses and elephants formed various layers of the *Chakravyuh*.

Yudhishthira and Bhima saw the *Chakravyuh* and got worried. Only Arjuna knew how to break through the formation. But he was at the other end of the battlefield fighting soldiers. They did not know what to do.

Abhimanyu was Arjuna's brave young son. Yudhishthira went to Abhimanyu and asked, 'Son, do you know how to break through the *Chakravyuh* like your father?'

Abhimanyu replied, 'I know how to enter the layers but I do not know how to exit it, Uncle. But do not worry,' he said with his eyes shining. 'Keep the army close to me. I will enter it and we will together fight our way out.'

Yudhishthira blessed the courageous boy.

So young Abhimanyu entered the many layers of the *Chakravyuh* fearlessly. The Kauravas were shocked! King Jayadratha ordered his soldiers to block Abhimanyu so that he would not be able to leave the formation. Hundreds of soldiers attacked Abhimanyu from all sides.

Alone, Abhimanyu fought and fought, but soon his shield and armour were broken. He lost his weapons. He lifted the wheel of his chariot and fought with it. But the Kauravas broke the wheel in a hundred pieces and killed the brave Abhimanyu.

# SUDARSHAN CHAKRA

Arjuna got to know about Abhimanyu's death that night. His heart broke and he wept. Then his sorrow turned to anger and he vowed, 'I will destroy all those who have killed my son!'
Yudhishthira said, 'King Jayadratha is the cause of Abhimanyu's death.'

'I will destroy him before sunset tomorrow. If I am unable to do that, I will kill myself right there,' Arjuna promised, his eyes glowing like fire.

It was now the fourteenth day of war. Dronacharya got to know of the promise Arjuna had made. This time, he arranged his soldiers in a triple *Chakravyuh*.

Arjuna charged furiously and broke through all the layers of the *Chakravyuh*. He fought fiercely with Dronacharya, Duryodhana and the other Kaurava warriors.

The sun had now begun to dip. The Kauravas knew that they had to ensure that King Jayadratha was safe till sunset. Then Arjuna would have to keep his promise and kill himself.

Krishna saw the sun dipping and rushed in. He raised his divine weapon, the *Sudarshan Chakra*, and covered the sun completely with it. Suddenly, the sky darkened and it looked as if night had fallen.

King Jayadratha saw the sky suddenly getting dark. He did not understand. He raised his head to look up at the sky. Immediately, Krishna moved the *Sudarshan Chakra* away and the sun came out. Arjuna saw King Jayadratha's head and preprared to attack him.

He shot an arrow straight at King Jayadratha and killed him. Arjuna had kept his promise and taken revenge for the death of his son, Abhimanyu.

The next day, Arjuna said worriedly, 'Dronacharya is the most skilled in the art of warfare. He is still alive. But how can we kill him? He is our guru!'

The next day, Bhima killed an elephant called Ashwatthama. The news that Ashwatthama had been killed by Bhima reached Dronacharya.

He did not know it was the elephant that had died. He thought his son Ashwatthama was dead. He laid down his weapons and left the battlefield, heartbroken.

# KARNA, THE NEW CHIEF

Lord Indra was Arjuna's father. He knew of Karna's strength and thought that Karna might defeat Arjuna in the war. Indra also knew of Karna's magic armour. He had a plan.

Lord Indra disguised himself as a poor brahmin and begged Karna to give him the golden armour.

Karna knew that all his strength and powers lay in his armour. But he never refused anyone who came to him for alms. So, he took off his armour and gave it to the brahmin. Lord Indra was deeply touched by Karna's selflessness.

Karna came to be known as Daata Karna.

The next morning, Karna and Arjuna faced each other in the battlefield. Bhima and Dushasana also attacked each other. After a long battle, Bhima killed Dushasana.

Karna and Arjuna fought each other mightily. Even the Gods came down to witness the two great warriors fight. Nobody had ever seen such a powerful show of strength.

Suddenly, Karna's chariot wheel got stuck in the mud and broke. He jumped off his chariot and bent to lift its wheel. Instinctively, Arjuna aimed an arrow to attack Karna but stopped. He said to Krishna, 'Karna is an unarmed warrior. It is against my values to attack someone who has no weapons.'

But Krishna replied, 'The Kauravas cheated you in the game of dice! They took away your kingdom and sent you to exile for thirteen years! They have given your brothers and your wife Draupadi so much misery! Do not spare Karna! ATTACK!'

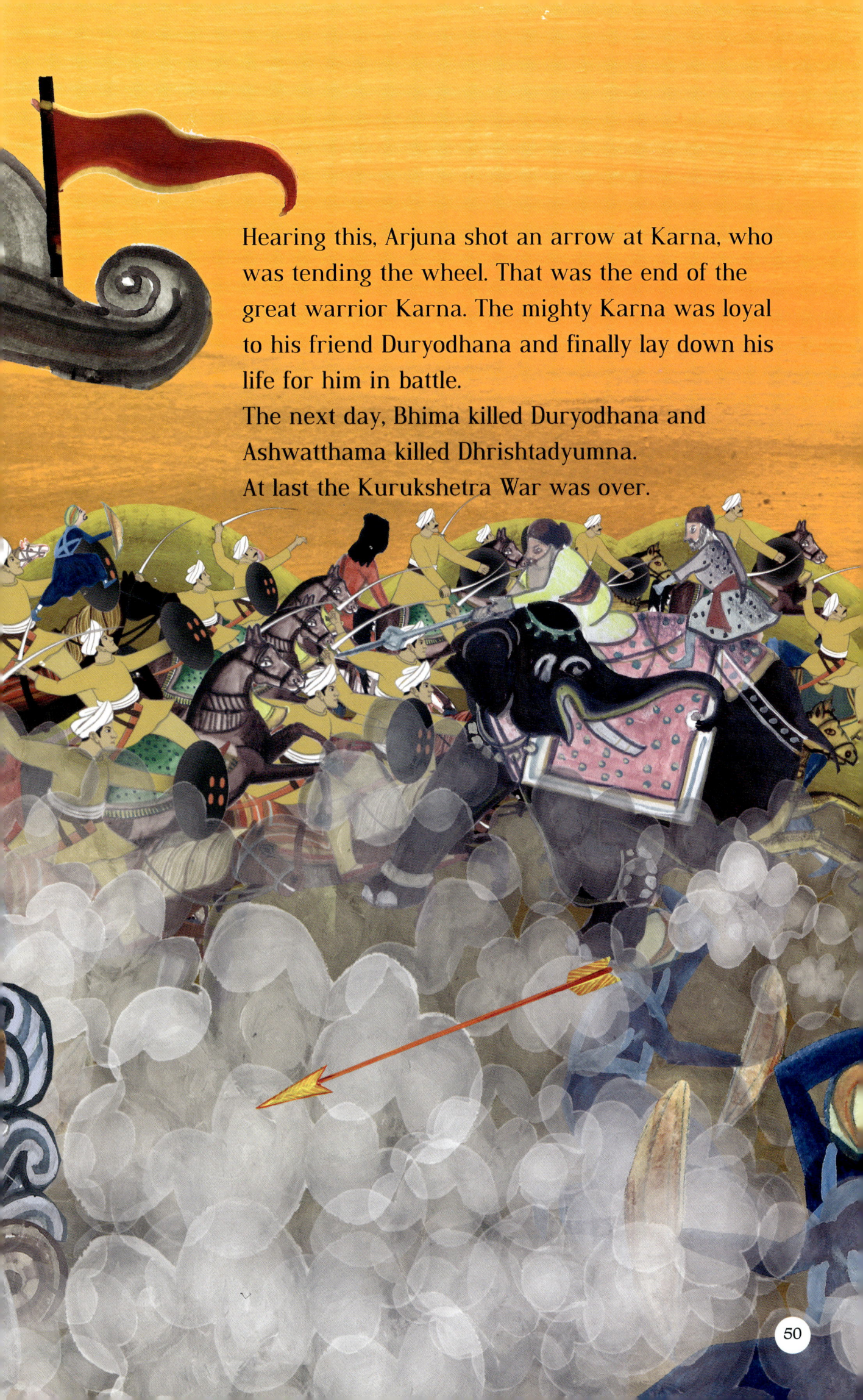

Hearing this, Arjuna shot an arrow at Karna, who was tending the wheel. That was the end of the great warrior Karna. The mighty Karna was loyal to his friend Duryodhana and finally lay down his life for him in battle.

The next day, Bhima killed Duryodhana and Ashwatthama killed Dhrishtadyumna.

At last the Kurukshetra War was over.

The war had lasted for eighteen days. The Pandavas and Draupadi were alive but had lost all their family and friends. They took Dhrithrashtra and Gandhari with them and left for Hastinapur.

Yudhishthira became the King of Hastinapur. He brought back peace and happiness to the people of his kingdom once again.

# TITLES IN THIS SERIES

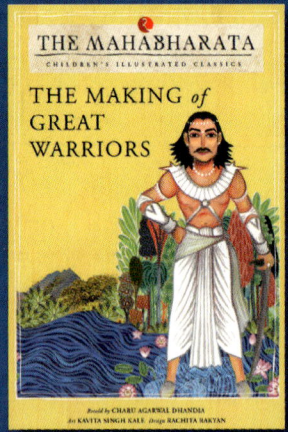
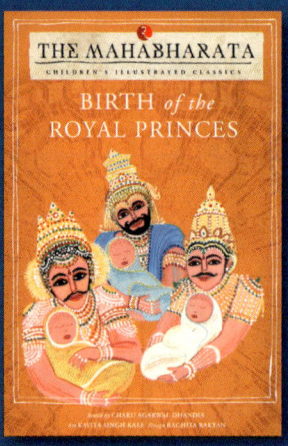
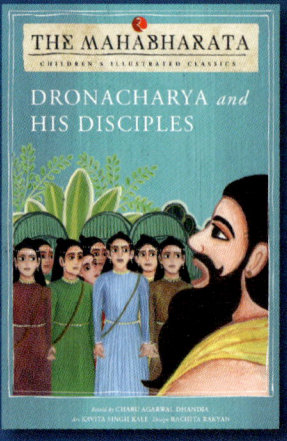
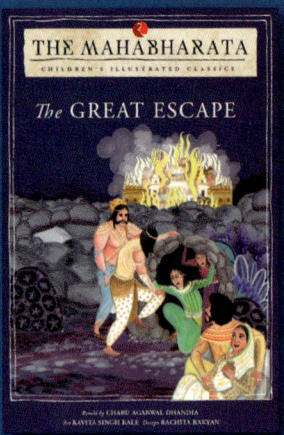
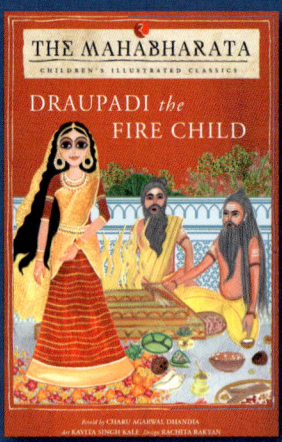
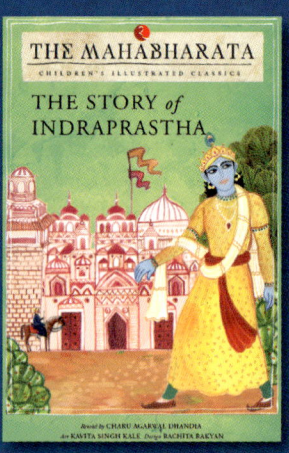
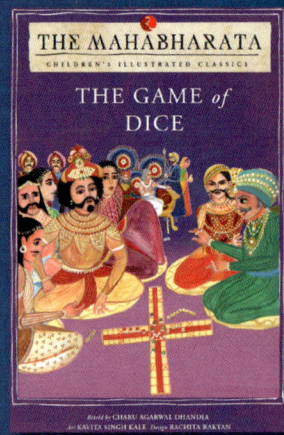
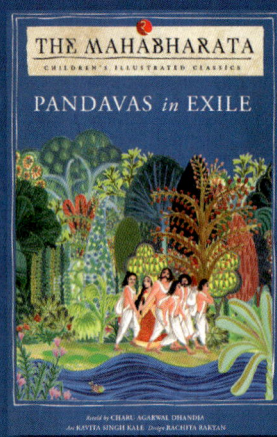
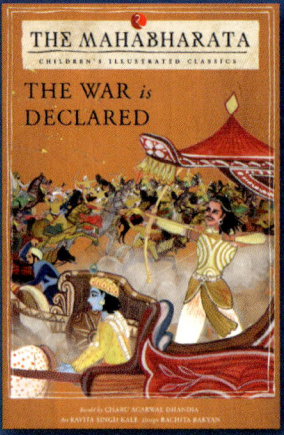

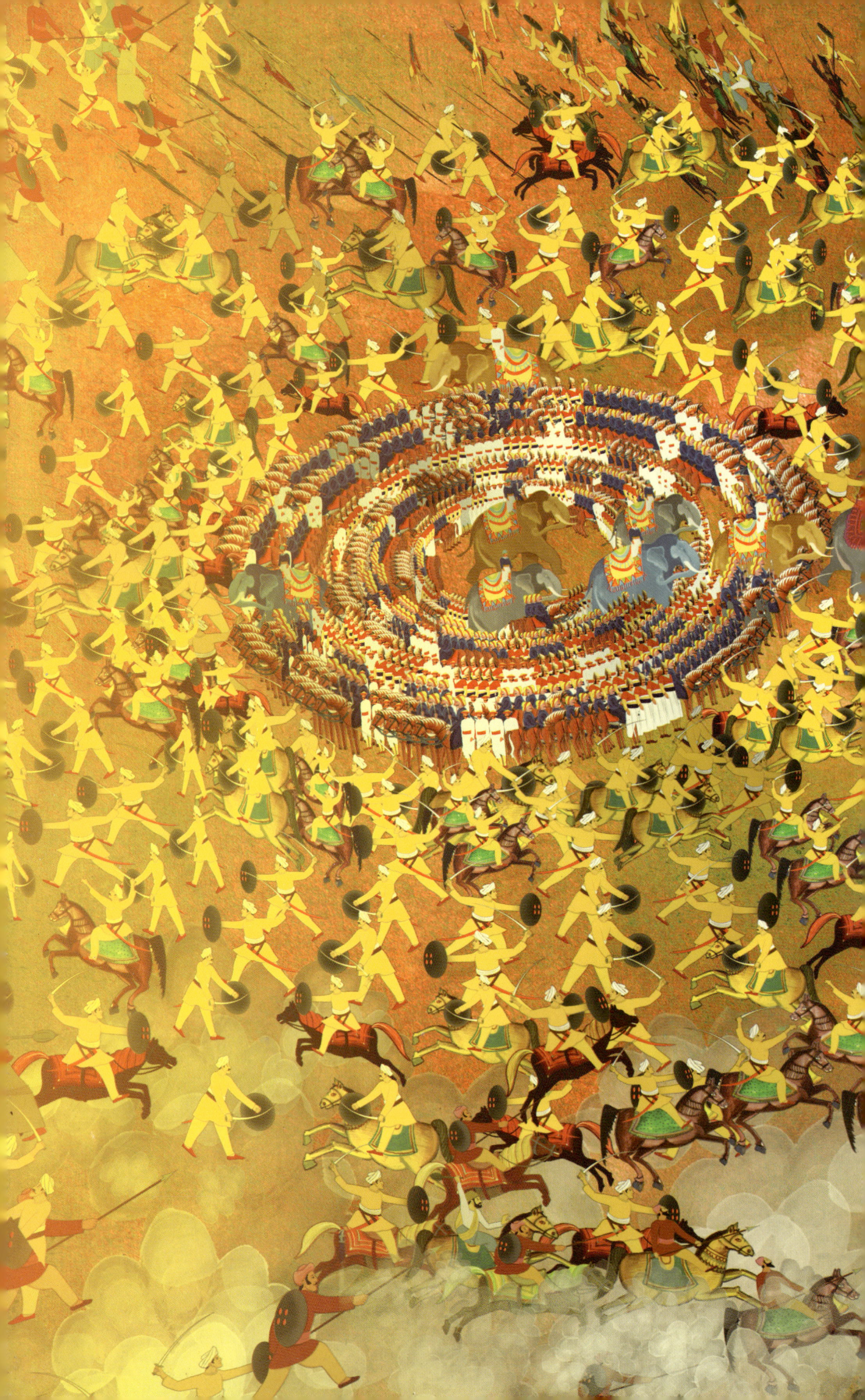